ENGLISH NINETEENTH CENTURY CAMEO GLASS

ENGLISH
NINETEENTH
CENTURY
CAMEO
GLASS

From the Collection of Mr. and Mrs. Albert Christian Revi

A SPECIAL EXHIBITION / 1963

THE CORNING MUSEUM OF GLASS
CORNING GLASS CENTER, CORNING, NEW YORK

PREFACE Few glass decorative techniques are more mysterious to the onlooker than cameo carving; few so greatly challenge the talent and skill of the glassmaker as technician and artist; and few can cause more hidden tensions in the object, wrought with such exacting care, which militate against its ultimate preservation. In the whole span of the history of glass only two periods have witnessed the combination of technical skill and artistic aim which enabled this exacting technique to flourish: the first century B.C. to the first century A.D. in Alexandria and possibly Rome, and the nineteenth in the glass district of Stourbridge in England.

The development of the glass cameo technique is the culmination of three long traditions: the near millennium and a half during which glassmakers strove to emulate in glass rare or semiprecious substances; the final flowering of a tradition of luxury cut glass which had its inception as early as the reign of Sargon II; the tradition of the lapidary who had until then directed his energies to cutting semiprecious stones such as the Gemma Augustea in onyx now preserved in the Kunsthistorisches Museum in Vienna.

When and where the first glass cameo was made is yet unknown. It seems certain, however, that by the end of the first century B.C. the technique had been mastered to an extent which has never been exceeded and barely approached.

In principle the technique is simple. A glass of one color is overlayed with one or more layers of glass of different colors having a similar coefficient of expansion. The outer layer or layers are carved by lapidary means until the desired design is achieved. Possibly the

5

1

2

3

6

best known classical example is the famed Barberini or Portland Vase (Fig. 1), discovered at the end of the sixteenth century and which since the early nineteenth century has been one of the glories of the British Museum.

We do not know what abrasives were used by the Roman or Alexandrian craftsmen, nor do we know what metals were employed to make the wheels and styli used to carve the most intricate details. They, however, permitted an intricacy of style and richness of decor which is evidenced in the small glass cup once in the collection of J. Pierpont Morgan (Fig. 3), or in the fragment of a standing figure crowned with a laurel leaf in a six layered cameo of blue, white, red, and green (Fig. 2).

For centuries after the fall of Rome the technique was forgotten and the idea of overlaying a glass of one color with glasses of another was abandoned. It recurred in the first half of the nineteenth century, mostly in factories operating in the Bohemian idiom. Intricate designs were carved in thick blanks overlaid with heavy multicolored layers often creating ponderous and somewhat gaudy masses.

The triumphant revival of the technique as it had been known to the Romans took place in England in the second half of the nineteenth century. No doubt this development was stimulated by the fame of the Portland Vase and by the extraordinary enthusiasm which had led Josiah Wedgwood to spend several years and untold effort in duplicating the glass masterpiece in ceramics. Eighteenth and nineteenth century collectors were particularly fascinated by the intricacies of cameos and gave James Tassie and his nephew William a mar-

7

ket for the prodigious quantities of glass paste cameos which they produced from the second half of the eighteenth century well into the nineteenth.

This exhibition is a tribute to this English revival and presents some of the finest pieces of English cameo glass preserved in America. They have been generously loaned to The Corning Museum of Glass by Mr. and Mrs. Albert Christian Revi of Dallas; one of the great pioneers in the cameo glass revival, Mr. Frederick Carder of Corning; The Metropolitan Museum of Art, New York City; Alfred University, Alfred, New York; Abraham and May, Granville, Massachusetts; and the Rockwell Foundation, Corning.

Through these pieces can be followed the stylistic evolution from the solid sculptural definitions of Joseph Locke to the sentimentally evocative scenes of George Woodall, and the technical changes made possible in the appearance of the glass through the introduction of acid etching combined with lapidary methods.

The Corning Museum of Glass expresses its deep gratitude to Mr. and Mrs. Albert Christian Revi for sharing with us their magnificent collection as well as to the other lenders mentioned above. In addition, we are indebted to Mr. Revi for providing the introduction to this catalogue.

Catalogue entries are based in part on information found in Geoffrey W. Beard's *Nineteenth Century Cameo Glass* and Mr. Revi's *Nineteenth Century Glass—Its Genesis and Development.*

PAUL N. PERROT, *Director*
The Corning Museum of Glass

INTRODUCTION

The revival of the ancient art of carving glass cameos began in England about 1860. At that time John Northwood of Wordsley (1836-1902) produced his first piece of cameo glass—a small vase having for its design a representation of Perseus rescuing Andromeda from the winged monster. Having proved his skill as a glass engraver, Northwood next attempted a sculptured crystal vase decorated with a frieze of Grecian horsemen after the fashion of the Elgin Marbles. In 1873 he began work on an exact copy of that most famous of all ancient glass cameos, the Portland Vase (Fig. 1). Working closely for three years with his cousin Philip Pargeter, the proprietor of the Red House Glass Works in Wordsley, Northwood finally completed his task in 1876. Unfortunately before the job was done his copy (Fig. 4) cracked and broke into several pieces. Nevertheless, it was considered a remarkable feat for which Northwood received the praise and admiration of the entire English glass trade.

His most important glass cameo was made under the aegis of Thomas Wilkes Webb. In 1876 Northwood began work on the Pegasus (Dennis) Vase (Fig. 6). It was exhibited by Thomas Webb and Sons at the Paris Exhibition of 1878 in an unfinished state and was hailed as another Northwood triumph. After its completion in 1882 the vase was sold to Mrs. Mary Morgan through Tiffany & Company of New York.

Northwood also carved the Milton Vase and three tazzas for Philip Pargeter from blanks supplied to him from the Red House Glass Works. The Milton Vase illustrates Northwood's cameo glass interpretation of Adam and Eve and the Archangel Michael in the Garden

9

4

5

6

of Eden as described in Milton's *Paradise Lost*. The tazzas are adorned with a cameo head, one of Shakespeare (Fig. 5), of Newton, and of Flaxman, and were obviously modelled after Wedgwood portrait medallions of the late eighteenth century. All of John Northwood's glass cameos, with the exception of the Pegasus Vase, remained in the private collection of Philip Pargeter and his heirs.

When the public demanded their share of cameo glass, Stevens & Williams of Brierley Hill, Staffordshire, engaged the entire decorating works of J. & J. Northwood to satisfy their needs. John Northwood and his brother hired as many skilled engravers and cutters of glass as were available in the district and produced a multitude of beautiful cameo glass objects. These productions, while not on a par with the hand-sculptured pieces made a few years earlier, were nevertheless fine examples of the glassmaker's art. In the beginning the work was a one-man operation from start to finish. As the need for a more accelerated rate of production manifested itself the work developed into a combined effort of the etcher, engraver and finisher, and thereby hangs the tale of its ultimate decline in quality.

In spite of what could be called mass production of cameo glass, some very fine works were turned out by such artist-engravers as William and Charles Northwood (John Northwood's nephews), Frederick Carder (No. 1 and Fig. 8), W. O. Bowen, James Hill, Joshua Hodgetts and B. Fenn. John Northwood II followed in his father's footsteps and produced an exceptional cameo glass plaque entitled "Aphrodite," and another smaller plaque "Dancing Figures" copied from a Wedgwood plaque by Flaxman.

11

Between 1880 and 1890 the art had deteriorated somewhat and very few fine examples of cameo work were produced in the Stourbridge District. Novelty wares, like "Dolce Relievo," which were produced by etching designs in various thicknesses on cased colored blanks, made their appearance in the showrooms of Stevens & Williams. The delicacy of the designs and color combinations found on some pieces of "Dolce Relievo" are exceptions in the general trend leading to poorer quality. They also produced cased colored blanks consisting of two or more contrasting colors sculptured with fruit and flower subjects with a realism not matched by the cameo artists of the later Art Nouveau period. These, too, are fine representations of English cameo glass.

A Frenchman, Alphonse Lechevrel, was engaged by Hodgetts, Richardson & Company of Wordsley specifically to teach a group of their engravers the art of carving cameo glass. His background as a medallist seems to have fitted him well for this task, for several fine glass cameos were produced by him and his most apt pupil, Joseph Locke (1846-1936). Like Northwood, Lechevrel produced comparatively few glass cameos, but every one of these is a work of art. "Raising an Altar to Bacchus" and "Hercules Restoring Alcestis to Her Husband" are his finest works and overshadow in size and design a pair of vases engraved by Lechevrel, and later altered by Woodall, entitled "The Birth of Venus" (No. 2), and "Venus Rising from the Sea."

Joseph Locke carved a facsimile of the Portland Vase for Hodgetts, Richardson & Company who exhibited it at the Paris Exhibition of

1878 where it won the Gold Medal award. Forty cased glass blanks, white on cobalt blue, were made, and of this number thirty-seven broke in the annealing process (No. 4). Work was commenced on number thirty-eight but this too was found to be faulty after several weeks of work had been spent upon it. He immediately began to work on the thirty-ninth blank and completed his perfectly sonorous replica of the Portland Vase in 1878 after about one year of concentrated work (No. 5). Locke's copy of the famous Roman urn is remarkable for its high relief rendition of the Portland designs in opal glass on a dark blue ground; in some places the cameo decoration approaches a three dimensional feeling. While it is true that Locke spent about one-third of the time Northwood expended on his version of the Portland Vase, we must take into consideration that Northwood's work on the vase was punctuated with interruptions caused by his business, making it necessary for him to work on his task at odd moments and during the evening hours.

Locke produced other pieces in the traditional style which emulated the ancient glass cameos: "Cupid Sailing in a Cockle Shell"; a pair of vases depicting putti dancing and playing on musical instruments; and a pair of covered vases with cameo relief decorations of Cupid on a Lion (modelled after a bas relief by Rietschel of Dresden which was exhibited at the Crystal Palace Exhibition of 1851). Locke's rendition of "Happy Childhood" and "Unhappy Childhood" (No. 3) on a pair of handled vases was obviously inspired by the work of the Belgian sculptor Simonis, who exhibited a pair of life-size marble statues of these subjects at the Crystal Palace Exhibition.

In these early works produced by Lechevrel and Locke the influence of ancient examples is apparent. In each case the design is modelled in white opal glass on a dark or plain colored background without the pictorial effects and shadings of light and dark that we find in later works by Woodall and his contemporaries.

Very little of what has been termed "commercial" cameo glass is in evidence from the factory of Hodgetts, Richardson & Company and their successors. Undoubtedly their productions were few by comparison with the output of Thomas Webb & Sons and Stevens & Williams.

A cameo glass vase in the Toledo Museum of Art collection has been attributed to Joseph Locke at a time when he was employed in America by Edward D. Libbey. On examination we found the work to have been executed primarily by etching processes and it is devoid of any hand work of any consequence. A few pieces of this type of cameo glass, done in the style of the Art Nouveau, still exist in the collection of some of Locke's friends and relatives.

Thomas Webb & Sons of Stourbridge were undoubtedly responsible for the largest production of English cameo glass in the late nineteenth century. Their most famous artist in this field was George Woodall (1850-1925). George (Fig. 7) and his brother Thomas Woodall were encouraged in their art careers by their maternal uncle Thomas Bott, who was famous for his painting of figure and natural subjects in enamels. The brothers received their early cameo experience in the studios of J. & J. Northwood, where they had the advantage of being trained in the craft by John Northwood himself. In due course they were persuaded to join the firm of Thomas Webb & Sons and George and Thomas Woodall formed their own group of cameo glass artists which has since become known as the Gem Cameo team. This team of artist-engravers included James M. O'Fallon, Thomas Farmer, Harry Davies, Frances Smith, Jacob Facer, J. Fereday, Jules Barbe and a man named F. Kretschman. Each of these men was capable of producing a glass cameo from start to finish, but they pooled their talents instead, and as a result of this merger many beautiful examples of cameo glass left the Webb factory marked "Gem Cameo" (Fig. 11).

In the meantime George Woodall produced several superb glass cameos; most of these were subscribed for before they were completed. Woodall developed his skill with the engraver's tools to the fullest, achieving shadings of light and dark which enabled him to depict the roundness of flesh, architectural effects, and landscapes with scope and perspective; even the smallest details in his works were executed with a meticulous sense for accuracy. He carried to a greater extent than any other what might be termed the "pictorial effect" in cameo work and gained the reputation among his contemporaries for being the finest cameo glass artist of their time.

A few Woodall cameos were the joint effort of George and his brother. It is believed that Thomas executed the borders of those articles signed "T. & G. Woodall," but he was a cameo artist in his own right and he may well have done portions or all of the figure work himself. "Flora" (No. 9) and "A Maid of Athens" (No. 12) are but two examples of the Woodall brothers' combined works.

George Woodall's greatest achievement in cameo glass is his

10

7

8

9

11

plaque the "Moorish Bathers" (No. 11) which he finished in 1898. It had been in production since about 1890 and was purchased on completion by the Hon. George Brookman of Adelaide, Australia. The "Moorish Bathers" nearly met somewhat the same fate that befell Woodall's "Aurora" Vase. Mrs. Nan Brookman's son, at that time but ten years old, saved the plaque from a fire which completely destroyed their home in Adelaide many years ago. The "Aurora" Vase was rescued from a sunken ship only to be destroyed in a fire a few years later. Until the "Moorish Bathers" had been produced the "Aurora" Vase, with its faithful rendition of Guido Reni's painting, had always been considered Woodall's finest work. In 1912 Woodall stated, in a newspaper interview, that his plaque, the "Moorish Bathers," was the finest thing he had ever done.

The team of Kretschman and Barbe produced some exceptionally fine examples of engraved, etched, and enameled cameo glass. One piece in our collection is decorated with tiny flowers and leaves in shallow relief enamelled in several shades of rose and green, and is further embellished with realistically painted rubies in square and triangular shapes all heavily encrusted with gold (No. 16). This team's version of "Happy Childhood and Unhappy Childhood" (No. 17) combines Webb's patented technique for simulating carved ivory (patented in England by Thomas Wilkes Webb, November 30, 1887, and in the United States on February 19, 1889) with such interesting features as applied glass windows and enamel and gold decorations. The windows were formed from a heat-sensitive glass which was blown into a mold to produce the effect of mullions. It was then reheated and the raised struts turned opalescent, thereby giving the appearance of small panes of glass set within a round casement.

Exceptionally large pieces were made by the Gem Cameo team. A very tall vase cut from a cased colored blank, rose on white, on blue (No. 18), can be found among the objects in the exhibition. The vase is not only beautiful in color and design, it is also skillfully sculptured and some of the leaves and flowers are almost three dimensional. Several insects are included in the design and have been carved with a faithfulness one would only expect from an entomologist. A huge cameo glass punch bowl in the collection of Thomas Goode & Co., London (Fig. 10), has been engraved from four layers of glass—dark green, pink, white, and light green. The bowl and its separate pedestal base stands 16″ high and the diameter of the bowl itself is 19″.

Among the novelty types of cameo glass produced by the Woodall team were interesting examples done in the style of Ch'ien Lung cameo glass (No. 27). The cameo reliefs, while emulating their Chinese prototypes, were made by utilizing an ancient technique known as "padding." Small pads or blobs of colored glass were placed on the body of the article wherever the cameo designs were to be executed. The pads of glass were then cut and engraved into fruit, flower, figure, animal and fish designs and the finished article was very often decorated with gold.

Very late in the cameo glass era, when the art had deteriorated greatly because the demand could not be met with objects on which much time and work had to be spent, Thomas Webb & Sons produced etched cameo relief designs on Pearl Satin glass (No. 20). The one saving grace is that most of these wares are beautiful in color and design.

The end of the production of fine cameo glass was hastened even more by the appearance on the market of "Lace de Bohême Cameo" and "Florentine Art Cameo" which were cheaply made copies of English cameo glass produced by painting designs in heavy white enamel on colored glass articles. The glass factories in Steinschönau in Bohemia produced quantities of what is now called "Mary Gregory glass" in imitation of English cameo glass, administering the *coup de grace* to an important phase of English glassmaking.

A. C. REVI

No. 1

"The Immortality of the Arts," by Frederick
Carder, after La Mercie. 1887, Brierley Hill,
blank blown at Stevens and Williams. Amber glass with opaque white overlay. D. 13″
(33.0 cm). Beard, Pl. XXI, Fig. 81. Carder
Collection.

No. 2

"The Birth of Venus," signed "Geo. Wood-all." An earlier signature "AL 1877" has been obliterated and a pair of handles re-moved. 1877, Wordsley, blank by Hodgetts, Richardson and Co., designed and engraved by Alphonse Lechevrel. Handles removed, and additional cutting by George Woodall perhaps as late as 1923. Engraved on base: "The Birth of Venus." Deep blue glass with opaque white overlay. H. 11⅛" (28.2 cm). Beard, Pl. XIX, Fig. 75; Revi, p. 136. Revi Collection.

No. 3

"Happy Childhood" and "Unhappy Childhood" Vases, by Joseph Locke. Signed "J.L.
1877," Wordsley, Hodgetts, Richardson and
Co. Deep blue glass overlayed with opaque
white. H. 9″ (22.8 cm). Abraham and May,
Granville, Mass. (Photograph courtesy
Delomosne and Son, Ltd., London.)

No. 4
Blank for Joseph Locke's "Portland" Vase. 1878, Wordsley, Hodgetts, Richardson and Co. Deep blue glass overlayed with opaque white. H. 9⅞″ (25.1 cm). Revi Collection.

No. 5

The "Portland" Vase, signed "Joseph Locke, 1878." Wordsley, blank produced at Hodgetts, Richardson and Co. H. 9⅞" (25.1 cm). Beard Pl. XXIII, Fig. 88; Revi, p. 138. Revi Collection.

Right, Base of Locke's "Portland" Vase.

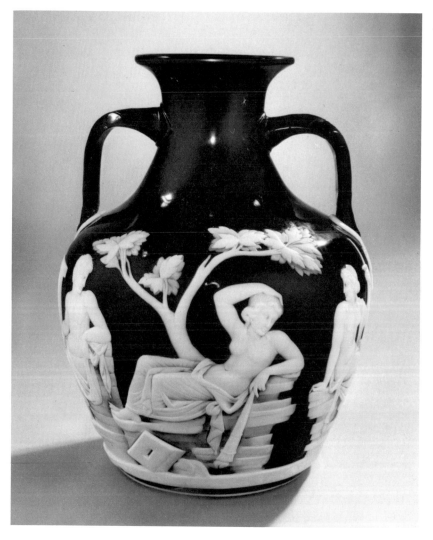

No. 6

"Hercules and the Lion," piece from one of
the broken blanks made for the Locke
"Portland" Vase. Probably 1878, Wordsley,
Hodgetts, Richardson & Co. Unfinished
engraving by Joseph Locke. Deep blue
glass with white overlay. D. 3¼″ (8.3 cm).
Revi Collection.

No. 7

Head, by Joseph Locke. About 1885.
Scratched on back ⚘. White on rose
beige. H. 1½″ (3.9 cm). Revi Collection.

No. 8

"Shakespeare" by Joseph Locke. Late 19th
century. Opaque white glass cemented on
a ruby base. H. 2⅞″ (7.3 cm). Beard, Pl.
XXII, Fig. 87. Alfred University. Gift of
Alexander Silverman.

No. 9

"Flora" signed "T. & G. Woodall." Late 19th-early 20th century, Stourbridge, Thomas Webb and Sons. Acid etched on back "Thomas Webb & Sons, Gem Cameo." "Webb." Puce with opaque white overlay. H. 11¾″ (29.8 cm). Beard, Pl. XIII, Fig. 50; Revi, p. 142. Revi Collection.

No. 10

"Aphrodite" signed "G. Woodall 1892."
Stourbridge, Thomas Webb & Sons. Acid
etched on base "Aphrodite" and "Thomas
Webb and Sons, Gem Cameo," "Webb."
Puce with opaque white overlay. D. 13⅛″
(33.3 cm). Beard, Pl. XII, Fig. 48; Revi,
p. 141. Revi Collection.

No. 11

"The Moorish Bathers," signed "Geo. Wood-
all." 1890 to 1898, Stourbridge, Thomas
Webb and Sons. Puce with opaque white
overlay. D. 18⅛″ (46.0 cm). Beard, Pl. XIV,
Fig. 54. Woodall considered the "Moorish
Bathers" his masterpiece. Revi Collection.

No. 12

"A Maid of Athens," signed "T. & G. Woodall." Late 19th century. Stourbridge, Thomas Webb and Sons. Acid etched on base "A
Maid of Athens," "Webb." Puce with
opaque white overlay. H. 10⅛" (25.7 cm).
Beard, p. 85; Revi, p. 143. Revi Collection.

No. 13

"Night," signed "G. Woodall." 1900, Stourbridge, Thomas Webb and Sons. Engraved
on base: "Night." Puce with opaque white
overlay. H. 8⅜" (21.3 cm). Beard, Pl. VIII,
Fig. 30. Revi Collection.

No. 14

Vase with a dancing figure, signed "G. Woodall." Late 19th century, Stourbridge, Thomas Webb and Sons. Turquoise blue with white overlay. H. 8⅞" (21.4 cm). Beard, Pl. XVI, Fig. 62. The Metropolitan Museum of Art, New York. Gift of Ethel Lyman Mackey and Ruth Watrous Hellum, 1960. (No. 60.7.)

No. 15

Vase, signed "G. Woodall." Late 19th-early 20th century, Stourbridge, Thomas Webb and Sons. Acid etched on base "Thomas Webb & Sons, Gem Cameo." Turquoise blue with opaque white and red overlay. H. 8⅜" (21.3 cm). Revi, p. 143. Revi Collection.

No. 16

Enameled and gilt vase. About 1885, Stourbridge, Thomas Webb & Sons, probably enameled by Jules Barbe. Acid etched on base, "Thomas Webb & Sons, Gem Cameo." Opaque white with enameling in shades of rose, green, red and encrusted with gold. H. 8″ (20.3 cm). Revi, p. 146. Revi Collection.

No. 17

"Happy Childhood and Unhappy Childhood." About 1877, Stourbridge, Thomas Webb and Sons. Acid etched on base "Webb." Ivory with red, brown, green and gold. H. 8¾″ (22.2 cm). The windows are of a glass which turned opalescent upon reheating. Revi, p. 150. Revi Collection.

No. 18

Vase. About 1885, Stourbridge, Thomas
Webb and Sons. Blue with rose and white
overlay. H. 18½″ (47.0 cm). Revi, p. 145.
Revi Collection.

No. 19

Vase with peony and prunus sprays. Late
19th century, Stourbridge, Thomas Webb
and Sons. Red with opaque white overlay.
H. 5⅞″ (14.9 cm). Beard, Pl. XX, Fig. 77.
The Metropolitan Museum of Art, New
York. Bequest of Mrs. James H. Wickes,
1906. (No. 06.126.)

No. 20
Pearl Satin rose bowl. 1889, Stourbridge,
Thomas Webb and Sons. Pale blue pearl
ware with opaque white overlay. H. 3⅜″
(8.6 cm). Revi, p. 8. Revi Collection.

No. 21
Covered jar. Late 19th century, England.
White, overlayed with yellow, pale red, and
gilt. H. with metal cover 8¾″ (22.2 cm).
Revi Collection.

No. 22

"Tailor bird feeding its young." About 1886, Brierley Hill, Stevens and Williams, designed by Frederick Carder. Citron with opaque white overlay. H. 6⅜″ (16.2 cm). Revi, p. 132. Revi Collection.

No. 23

Vase. About 1880-1890, Brierley Hill, Stevens and Williams, designed by Frederick Carder. Deep rose with opaque white overlay. H. 6⅞″ (17.5 cm). The Rockwell Foundation, Corning.

No. 24

Vase. About 1880-1890. Brierley Hill, Stevens and Williams, designed by Frederick Carder. Citron with white overlay. Acid etched on base: "Stevens and Williams, Stourbridge, Art Glass." H. 9⅞" (25.6 cm). The Rockwell Foundation, Corning.

No. 25

Pitcher. About 1880, England. Red acid
etched background with opaque white overlay. H. 6⅛″ (15.6 cm). Revi, p. 147. Revi
Collection.

No. 26
"Two Muses," by William Northwood.
About 1889, Wordsley, J. & J. Northwood.
Amber with opaque white overlay. H. 4⅛″
(10.5 cm). Revi, p. 133. Revi Collection.

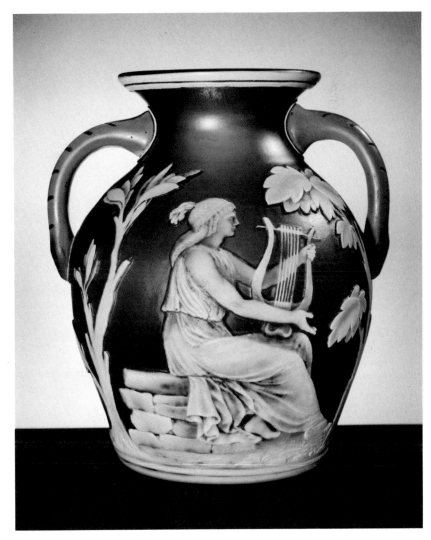

No. 27

Vase in Chinese "Ch'ien Lung" style, engraved by Daniel and Lionel Pearce. About 1885. Stourbridge, Thomas Webb and Sons. Acid etched on base "Webb." Pink with green, red, brown, and gilt applied blobs. H. 5⅞" (15.0 cm). Revi, p. 152. Revi Collection.